"Little Bit of Heaven"

A Baby's Book

A written heirloom

recording the special moments

and treasured experiences

of our child's early years.

Birth Through Kindergarten

Illustrations by Bessie Pease Gutmann

NELSON/REGENCY

"*Blossom Time*"

Illustrations by Bessie Pease Gutmann

ISBN: 0-8407-3775-0

Anticipation!

Date my pregnancy was confirmed _____

Probable due date _____

What we did to celebrate _____

_____

Our hopes for you _____

_____

When and where your movement was first felt _____

_____

Classes taken and books read _____

_____

Other special times while anticipating your birth _____

_____

_____

_____

Comments and care advice

Who _____ What _____

_____

Who _____ What _____

_____

Who _____ What _____

_____

Who _____ What _____

_____

Who _____ What _____

Our Baby's First Photos

(baby's first photos here)

Our Family Tree

The names and birthdates of your

_____ _____ _____ _____ _____ _____ _____ _____

| Great Grandma | Great Grandpa | Great Grandma | Great Grandpa | Great Grandma | Great Grandpa | Great Grandma | Great Grandpa |

_____ _____

Grandma　　　　　　*Grandpa*　　　　　　*Grandma*　　　　　　*Grandpa*

_____ _____

Mother　　　　　　　　　　　　*Father*

_____

Self

_____ _____

_____ _____

_____ _____

_____ _____

_____ _____

Sisters　　　　　　　　　　　　*Brothers*

Useful Gifts and Thoughtful Celebrations

Celebration _____

Hostess / Host _____ Date _____

Guests and Gifts _____

_____

_____

_____

_____

_____

_____

Celebration _____

Hostess / Host _____ Date _____

Guests and Gifts _____

_____

_____

_____

_____

_____

_____

Celebration _____

Hostess / Host _____ Date _____

Guests and Gifts _____

_____

_____

_____

_____

A Beautiful Baby's Birth

Birthdate _____ Day of the week _____ Time _____

Birthplace _____

Weight _____ Length _____ Eye color _____

Hair color and quantity _____

_____

Distinctive characteristics _____

_____

_____

_____

Whom you first looked like _____

_____

_____

_____

How Mom got to the delivery room _____

_____

_____

_____

Delivered by _____

Test results _____

_____

_____

_____

_____

_____

Birth Day Mementos

(baby's hospital I. D. bracelet here)

(newspaper clipping announcing birth here)

(birth announcement here)

Copy of Birth Certificate

(copy of certificate here)

"Contentment"

A Beautiful Little Person

What's In a Name?

Your full name _____

Nicknames _____

_____

Meaning or origin of your name _____

_____

_____

Why we chose this special name _____

_____

_____

_____

Religious Ceremony _____

Church _____

Type of ceremony _____

Date _____ Clergy _____

Special scripture _____

Special prayer _____

Notes _____

_____

_____

_____

_____

"His Majesty"

A Beautiful Baby's Development Diary

Your First Month

Length _____   Weight _____

Physical changes _____

_____

_____

Eating and sleeping habits _____

_____

_____

New skills, accomplishments and talents _____

_____

_____

New places visited and new experiences _____

_____

_____

Your favorite. . .

Toys _____   Colors _____

Music _____   Other _____

Activities _____

_____

_____

Other notes _____

_____

_____

_____

Your Second Month

Length _____ Weight _____

Physical changes _____

_____

_____

Eating and sleeping habits _____

_____

_____

New skills, accomplishments and talents _____

_____

_____

New places visited and new experiences _____

_____

_____

Your favorite . . .

Toys _____ Colors _____

Music _____ Other _____

Activities _____

_____

_____

_____

Other notes _____

_____

_____

_____

Your Third Month

Length _____ Weight _____

Physical changes _____

_____

_____

Eating and sleeping habits _____

_____

_____

New skills, accomplishments and talents _____

_____

_____

New places visited and new experiences _____

_____

_____

Your favorite . . .

Toys _____ Colors _____

Music _____ Other _____

Activities _____

_____

_____

_____

Other notes _____

_____

_____

_____

"Mighty Like A Rose"

Your Fourth Month

Length _____ Weight _____

Physical changes _____

_____

_____

Eating and sleeping habits _____

_____

_____

New skills, accomplishments and talents _____

_____

_____

New places visited and new experiences _____

_____

_____

_____

Your favorite. . .

Toys _____ Colors _____

Music _____ Other _____

Activities _____

_____

_____

_____

Other notes _____

_____

_____

_____

Your Fifth Month

Length _____ Weight _____

Physical changes _____

_____

_____

Eating and sleeping habits _____

_____

_____

New skills, accomplishments and talents _____

_____

_____

New places visited and new experiences _____

_____

_____

Your favorite...

Toys _____ Colors _____

Music _____ Other _____

Activities _____

_____

_____

_____

Other notes _____

_____

_____

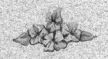

Your Sixth Month

Length_____ Weight _____

Physical changes _____

_____

_____

Eating and sleeping habits _____

_____

_____

New skills, accomplishments and talents _____

_____

_____

_____

New places visited and new experiences _____

_____

_____

_____

Your favorite . . .

Toys_____ Colors_____

Music_____ Other_____

Foods_____

Activities _____

_____

_____

Other notes _____

_____

_____

_____

"Chums"

Your Seventh Month

Length _____ Weight _____

Physical changes _____

_____

_____

Eating and sleeping habits _____

_____

_____

New skills, accomplishments and talents _____

_____

_____

New places visited and new experiences _____

_____

_____

Your favorite. . .

Toys _____ Colors _____

Music _____ Other _____

Foods _____

Activities _____

_____

_____

Other notes _____

_____

_____

Your Eighth Month

Length _____ Weight _____

Physical changes _____

_____

_____

Eating and sleeping habits _____

_____

_____

New skills, accomplishments and talents _____

_____

_____

New places visited and new experiences _____

_____

_____

Your favorite...

Toys _____ Colors _____

Music _____ Other _____

Foods _____

Activities _____

_____

_____

Other notes _____

_____

_____

_____

Your Ninth Month

Length _____ Weight _____

Physical changes _____

_____

_____

Eating and sleeping habits _____

_____

_____

New skills, accomplishments and talents _____

_____

_____

New places visited and new experiences _____

_____

_____

Your favorite. . .

Toys _____ Colors _____

Music _____ Other _____

Foods _____

Activities _____

_____

_____

Other notes _____

_____

_____

_____

"Mine"

Your Tenth Month

Length _____ Weight _____

Physical changes _____

_____

_____

Eating and sleeping habits _____

_____

_____

New skills, accomplishments and talents _____

_____

_____

New places visited and new experiences _____

_____

_____

Your favorite . . .

Toys _____ Colors _____

Music _____ Other _____

Foods _____

Activities _____

_____

_____

Other notes _____

_____

_____

_____

"Nitey Night"

Your Eleventh Month

Length _____ Weight _____

Physical changes _____

_____

_____

Eating and sleeping habits _____

_____

_____

New skills, accomplishments and talents _____

_____

_____

New places visited and new experiences _____

_____

_____

Your favorite. . .

Toys _____ Colors _____

Music _____ Other _____

Foods _____

Activities _____

_____

_____

Other notes _____

_____

_____

_____

Your First Year

Height _____ Weight _____

Physical changes _____

_____

_____

New skills, accomplishments and talents _____

_____

_____

New places we visited and new experiences _____

_____

Your favorite...

Toys _____ Colors _____

Songs _____ Foods _____

Clothing _____ Friends _____

Stories _____ Games _____

Activities/Other _____

_____

Biggest family events of the year _____

_____

_____

Biggest world events of the year _____

_____

_____

Other notes _____

_____

Your First Birthday

How we celebrated _____
_____
_____

Who was there _____
_____
_____

Decorations _____
_____

Cake _____
Gifts _____
_____
_____
_____

Notes _____
_____
_____
_____
_____
_____
_____
_____
_____
_____

(photo here)

Your Second Year

Height _____   Weight _____

New skills, accomplishments and talents _____

_____

_____

New places we visited _____

_____

Your favorite. . .

Toys _____   Colors _____

Songs _____   Foods _____

Clothing _____   Friends _____

Stories _____   Games _____

Activities / Other _____

_____

Your Second Birthday

How we celebrated _____

_____

Who was there _____

_____

_____

_____   (photo here)

_____

_____

Your Third Year

Height _____ Weight _____

New skills, accomplishments and talents _____

_____

_____

New places we visited _____

_____

Your favorite...

Toys _____ Colors _____

Songs _____ Foods _____

Clothing _____ Friends _____

Stories _____ Games _____

Activities/Other _____

_____

Your Third Birthday

How we celebrated _____

_____

Who was there _____

_____

_____

_____

_____

_____   (photo here)

_____

Your Fourth Year

Height _____ Weight _____

New skills, accomplishments and talents _____

_____

_____

New places we visited _____

_____

Your favorite. . .

Toys _____ Colors _____

Songs _____ Foods _____

Clothing _____ Friends _____

Stories _____ Games _____

Activities/Other _____

_____

Your Fourth Birthday

How we celebrated _____

_____

Who was there _____

_____

_____

_____

_____

_____

(photo here)

Your Fifth Year

Height _____ Weight _____

New skills, accomplishments and talents _____

_____

_____

New places we visited _____

_____

Your favorite . . .

Toys _____ Colors _____

Songs _____ Foods _____

Clothing _____ Friends _____

Stories _____ Games _____

Activities / Other _____

_____

Your Fifth Birthday

How we celebrated _____

_____

Who was there _____

_____

_____

_____   (photo here)

_____

_____

"Taps"

A Beautiful Baby Celebrates the Holidays

Your First Christmas _____

_____

On Christmas Eve, we _____

_____

_____

_____

On Christmas Day, we _____

_____

_____

_____

Loved ones who shared the holiday _____

_____

_____

Special gifts _____

_____

(first Christmas photo here)

Your Second Christmas _____

_____

On Christmas Eve, we _____

_____

_____

_____

On Christmas Day, we _____

_____

_____

_____

Loved ones who shared the holiday _____

_____

_____

Special gifts _____

_____

(second Christmas photo here)

Your Third Christmas _____

_____

On Christmas Eve, we _____

_____

_____

_____

On Christmas Day, we _____

_____

_____

_____

Loved ones who shared the holiday _____

_____

_____

Special gifts _____

_____

(third Christmas photo here)

"Asking For Trouble"

Your Fourth Christmas _____

_____

On Christmas Eve, we _____

_____

_____

_____

Christmas Day, we _____

_____

_____

_____

Loved ones who shared the holiday _____

_____

_____

Special gifts _____

_____

(fouth Christmas photo here)

Your Fifth Christmas _____

_____

On Christmas Eve, we _____

_____

_____

_____

On Christmas Day, we _____

_____

_____

_____

Loved ones who shared the holiday _____

_____

_____

Special gifts _____

_____

(fifth Christmas photo here)

Other Special Days and Holidays

_____

_____

_____

_____

_____

_____

_____

_____

_____

_____

_____

_____

_____

_____

_____

_____

_____

_____

_____

_____

_____